Allie's Adventure

From A to Z

by Ellen Dreyer
Illustrated by Jui Ishida

McGraw-Hill School Division

New York   Farmington

1

This is **Allie**.

Allie sees a **butterfly**.

Allie sees a **cow**.

Allie sees a **door**.

Allie sees some **eggs**.

Allie sees lots of **feathers**.

Allie pushes the **gate**.

Allie sees a **hole**.

Allie sees an **insect**.

Allie **jumps**!

A hole is no place for a **kitten**.

Allie sees some **lettuce**.

Allie does not see the **mouse**.

Allie sees a tiny **nose**.

She puts her paw **on** the nose.

The mouse runs past the **pumpkins!**

The mouse is very **quick**.

Allie needs a **rest**!

Allie curls up in a **sunny** spot.

She is very **tired**.

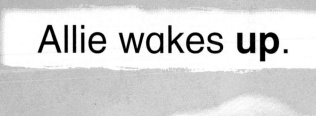

Allie wakes **up**.

She hears a **voice**.

Allie **walks** toward the voice.

Allie is **excited**.

A boy is **yelling** her name.

Zack missed Allie.